Published by Puffin Books Ltd 2013
A Penguin Company
Penguin Books Ltd, 80 Strand, London, WC2R 0RL, UK
Penguin Group (USA) Inc., 375 Hudson Street, New York 10014, USA
Penguin Books Australia Ltd, Camberwell Road, Camberwell, Victoria 3124,
Australia (A division of Pearson Australia Group Pty Ltd)
Penguin Group (NZ), 67 Apollo Drive, Rosedale, Auckland 0632,
New Zealand (a division of Pearson New Zealand Ltd)
Canada, India, South Africa

Written by Mandy Archer
Comic illustrations by Vincent Bechet
Comic text by Kieran Grant

© Mind Candy Ltd. Moshi Monsters is a trademark
of Mind Candy Ltd. All rights reserved.

www.puffin.co.uk

ISBN: 978-1-40939-219-4
001
Printed in Italy

PEARSON

ALWAYS LEARNING

Contents

Pirate Roll Call

I canna resist it any longer, there's a stirring in me old sea legs! Yer old mate Cap'n Buck is **getting ready to sail off into Potion Ocean.** I got me sights set on me favourite stretch of sea – Pirate Paradise. Arrr, it be a fine place and no mistake!

Anyways, enough jabbering, I've **got to get everything shipshape.** First on the list is recruiting me crew. **I've got me eye on a gang of waifs and strays** that I spotted lurking in the backstreets of Monstro City. A share of the booty should buy their time for this voyage. **Here's the scoop on every last one o' them...**

LEFTY is Buck's best mate, lookout and sea flood brother, all rolled into one! Many years ago the monster suffered an injury after a sword fight with a seagull, so now he sticks to the crow's nest. His one sharp eye can spot treasure from miles around. Lefty goes everywhere with Buck.

Pssst! Did you know that Buck wears his eye patch in honour of his mono-peepered pal, Lefty?

LEFTY

Buck would pay good money to have **PEPPY** on board, as long as the Birdy agrees to leave its motorbike at home. The Stunt Penguin has all the ingredients of a great pirate – Peppy's reckless and rebellious with a taste for pilchard popsicles. What's not to like?

PEPPY

SQUIDGE looks super-cute, but this Moshling isn't sweet in the slightest. The bloodsucking Furry Heebee is so teeth-chatteringly scary even pirates run in the opposite direction! Buck summons Squidge when he wants to put the frighteners on any advancing sea monsters.

SQUIDGE

Buck recruited **CHOP CHOP** when he dropped anchor on the edge of the Gombala Gombala Jungle. The playful primate pelted him with gooberries from a tree! The Captain thought this was the most hilarious thing he'd seen all year – now he always has a Cheeky Chimp on-board to keep the crew entertained.

CHOP CHOP

HANSEL

HANSEL is a rascal if ever we saw one! Captain Buck always tries to entice this half-baked hooligan onto his crew. Psycho Gingerboys are brilliant at bagging booty – sometimes they even use liquorice lassos to snag stash for the ship.

Lefty says that Pilfering Toucans are pirates with wings! **TIKI** can't resist 'borrowing' things – the barmy Birdy will even have your pocket money if you don't look sharp! Buck uses a bag of salty gobstoppers to keep the toucan in line. Tiki will do anything for a lick of a luscious sweet!

TIKI

JEEPERS

Snuggly Tiger Cubs have no place on a pirate ship. The soppy little critters aren't cut out for a life of sword fights, pillage and plank walking! Captain Buck, however, thinks **JEEPERS** is utterly adorable. He's smuggled the Moshling on board so he can feed the Beastie swoonafish tidbits every evening.

FREE ROX!

Legend has it that there are Rox to be plundered in these parts, but you've got to know where to look for them. Buck has scribbled eleven special numbers in his log books and strewn them across this annual. Write the numbers down in the order that they appear.

When you're done, sign into www.moshimonsters.com and click the Enter Secret Code button. Now enter the digits in order. The reward? A Roxilicious bag of booty for your Moshi!

7

PIECES OF ROX

Cap'n Buck has some **great memories** of his time in **Pirate Paradise**, but the old sea dog's a wee bit fuzzy on the details. **Can you remind him how to get to his dream destination?** *The Cloudy Cloth Clipper* will be sailing in circles unless something gets done!

Find some pens and pencils, then use this chart to **draw a map** from Monstro City all the way to Pirate Paradise. **The route can be as argh-mazing and fangtastical as your imagination!**

2

What incredible sights will the shipmates pass along the way? Will Lefty spy Spraytona Beach, Candy Shoals or somewhere completely new? **Draw in islands, whirlpools and distant ports,** then think up names for them all. Don't forget to fill the oceans with Batty Bubblefish, Songful SeaHorses and salty sea monsters, too! **Use a dotted line to show the Cap'n the best way to navigate through.**

X marks the spot!

N

NW NE

W E

SW SE

S

9

Port Pack Up

Avast, me hearties! The shipmates might be willing, the shipmates might be able, but **we won't be going anywhere til the *Cloudy Cloth Clipper* is loaded up with supplies.** I've got to splash out on crates of nosh, barrels of drink and all sorts of ship's stash! **I've written me a list** and **it ain't going to be cheap.** No matter, I'd wager that Babs would accept a piratey I.O.U if I flash her one of me grins!

Can you help Barnacle E. Buck **find all the items on his kit list?** There are **twelve essential objects hidden** in this word search grid. The cheeky little blighters could be running **in any direction, even back to front!** Use a pencil to circle every one.

A	D	J	S	S	A	L	G	Y	P	S	R	Y	X	E
C	R	O	A	K	C	O	N	U	T	J	U	I	C	E
C	X	I	U	U	B	S	Q	U	X	V	B	E	H	M
U	P	X	G	L	Z	N	M	W	O	T	B	X	G	J
D	W	I	Q	L	K	A	R	G	B	K	E	L	X	N
D	Z	M	D	A	B	P	N	I	X	B	R	A	S	R
L	G	N	F	N	P	P	X	A	O	Q	D	F	O	V
Y	Q	H	W	D	D	E	R	V	R	Z	U	H	I	Y
P	A	S	H	B	B	R	G	D	Y	P	C	K	T	Z
I	E	I	C	O	N	R	H	O	H	N	K	S	A	A
R	N	F	M	N	E	F	C	O	A	L	S	W	Z	C
A	J	Y	K	E	P	C	W	K	M	G	F	P	Q	J
T	U	I	N	S	T	I	U	S	G	N	I	V	I	D
E	T	E	N	T	A	C	L	E	C	H	A	I	R	E

BAB'S BOUTIQUE
1 SNAPPER for recording me adventures.
1 DIVING SUIT for jumping in the drink.

BIZARRE BAZAAR
1 ANCHOR so we don't go adrift.
1 ROX BOX for keeping me booty safe from thieving tentacles.
1 CUDDLY PIRATE cos they're totally irresistibubble!

HORRODS
1 SKULL AND BONES to show me pirate colours.
3 crates o' FISH-N-MIX for when the crew get peckish.
1 spare SPYGLASS for keeping a lookout.

THE GROSS-ERY STORE
4 barrels of CROAKCONUT JUICE for those long nights drifting at sea.
12 crates of GREEN for warding off the scurvy.

YUKEA
1 TENTACLE CHAIR for lounging in me cabin.
5 RUBBER DUCKS in a range of piratey patterns.

ONLY BUCK AND HIS PIRATE PALS CAN GET HOLD OF THIS BOOTY · IT'S NOT ALL AVAILABLE IN MONSTRO CITY!

DR. STRANGEGLOVE
Will See You Now...

What are the Dr.'s naughty intentions? The limelight-hogging villain has poured his plans into a song, and a fiendishly good one at that! Dr. Strangeglove might be a wrong'un, but he's a showbiz natural! He's even roped in all his Glump workers to join him. Moshlings turn away now – you aren't gonna like it!

Can you complete Dr. Strangeglove's devilishly difficult signature tune? Read each line, look at the picture clue, then fill in the missing lyrics.

The Doctor will see you now ... Mwah-ah-ah-ah-ah-aaa!

Sneaky, sly and shifty, let me introduce myself I'm the doctor they call _ _ _ _ _ _ _ _ _ _ _ _ , a hazard to your health!

I'm here to wreak some mayhem with my terrifying schemes, and glump your silly _ _ _ _ _ _ _ _ _ with my dastardly machines!

Glump chorus

Strangeglove, Strangeglove, they call him Dr. Strangeglove,

Strangeglove, Strangeglove, the one to be afraid of!

Strangeglove, Strangeglove, they call him Dr. Strangeglove,

Strangeglove, Strangeglove, Strangeglove, Strange

I assume you think it's sinister to hold an ancient grudge

But understand it cost my _ _ _ _ , so don't be quick to judge

A _ _ _ _ _ _ _ mangled it and chewed it like a shoe

He thought it was some _ _ _ _ _ _ _ _

so now this _ _ _ _ _ must do

Don't impede my evil deeds or try to foil my plans

Even though I wear this _ _ _ _ _ I have some helping hands

So peek outside your _ _ _ _ _ _ and check behind the _ _ _ _

Is Dr. _ _ _ _ _ _ _ _ _ _ _ lurking or has he called before?

Glump chorus

Let 'em have it, _ _ _ _ _ _ _ _ _!

Blow harder, you spherical fool!

I'll show those _ _ _ _ _ _ _ _ _ _

Oh yes, nasty!

Today Monstro City, tomorrow ... the world, the WORLD!!!

Racing Rascals and Rogues

Wicked **Dr. Strangeglove** won't rest 'til he's stirred up some **serious trouble.** The baddy is on a **mission to snatch the *Cloudy Cloth Clipper*** before Cap'n Buck gets back from the shops! There are Glumps bounding up and down the towers and tunnels of Monstro City. **Who will get back to the Port first?** Buck and his pirate pals have got a race on their paws!

STUMPED BY A GLUMP?
Fluff up your hair into a Fabio quiff.

STUMPED BY A GLUMP?
Do an impression of Fishlips on the trombone.

SUPER MOSHIS TO THE RESCUE!
Miss a turn.

STUMPED BY A GLUMP?
Find an object that's as blue as Bloopy.

STUMPED BY A GLUMP?
Do your meanest Freakface impression then cackle wickedly.

Finish

GLUMPATRON 3000 STARTS WORKING
Throw again.

STUMPED BY A GLUMP?
Make like Rocko and name three things you can't stand.

STUMPED BY A GLUMP?
Spell 'Black Jack' backwards.

STUMPED BY A GLUMP?
Show you're as tough as Bruiser by displaying your best wrestling move.

START

How to Play

1. Find a counter each to play with or choose your favourite Moshi figurines.

2. One of you must race for Cap'n Buck, the other for Dr. Strangeglove. Which one of you has the naughtiest streak? Nominate the most rascally rogue to play for the dastardly Doctor.

3. Choose the game board to match your character, then place your counter at the start.

4. Take turns throwing the die, moving your counter towards the *Cloudy Cloth Clipper* in the middle. When you land on a coloured challenge square, you must do the forfeit before moving forward again. Cap'n Buck is confronted by Glumps at every turn. Dr. Strangeglove has some serious pirate power to contend with!

5. The winner is the player who gets their counter to the finish first.

BEWARE OF PIRATES!
Find three objects that would be of no use to a pirate.

DR. STRANGEGLOVE GETS DISTRACTED BY A SECOND HAND MITTEN SALE.
Miss a turn.

BEWARE OF PIRATES!
Take your turn as if you're caught in a terrible sea storm.

BEWARE OF PIRATES!
Whistle a sea shanty.

BEWARE OF PIRATES!
Do your best Elder Furi impression.

Finish

BEWARE OF PIRATES!
Name two Fishies that live in the ocean deep.

BEWARE OF PIRATES!
Act out walking the plank.

BEWARE OF PIRATES!
Make your body as wibbly wobbly as Lefty.

BEWARE OF PIRATES!
Act as if there's a parrot on your shoulder.

START

Monstrous Nosh

Despite their rough and ready appearance, **pirates are sticklers for decent cooking.** Buck's crew can't climb the rigging all day without a **belly full of decent nosh** to keep them going! So what does a swashbuckling Monster like to munch on? **Sneak a peek at the menu . . .**

Picked and shipped from Candy Shoals!

Ye Old Menu
FOR THE
Epic Voyage TO Pirate Paradise

Days 1-7

Breakfast
Seaweed on toast washed down with a grimy glass of Sea Squash

Elevensies
Crab and Jelly Sandwich

Twelvsies
A pawful of Sunshine Berries and a generous lump of Green

Lots of stuff squashed into one delightful drink.

Luncheon
A whopping great slice of Eye Pie

Dinner
Sixty-two carrot medallions of Roast Beast served with a dollop of Jelly Baked Beans plus a pirate pud of Roarberry Cheesecake

Supper
Garlic Marshmallows roasted on deck

Grog
Flagons of Toad Soda, Snail Ale or Lefty Lemonade available all day and all night!

Ye Old Menu for the Epic Voyage to Pirate Paradise

Days 8-100

Baked Boot
Freshly caught by Billy Bob Baitman

and when all that runs out there's plenty of the pirate's old favourite. Slop, Slop, and yet more Slop

Batty Bubblefish! Must ration the grub and lock the galley door from now on.

Just make sure it don't run away from yer!

POSTCARDS From MONSTRO CITY

The *Cloudy Cloth Clipper* is **finally out on the open water!** I be glad to feel the wind in me fur and the salty taste of Potion Ocean at the back of me throat! **Now we're on course for Pirate Paradise** I can get down to beeswax - I've got a stack of postcards and letters to read from all me well-wishers back at Monstro City.

Sheesh! Buck is a first class ship's captain, but his filing is lousy! Right now he's using the *Clipper's* mail stack to prop up the leg of his wobbly desk. Can you pull out the letters and postcards and sort them into some kind of order? Read each of the messages, then use your Moshi know-how to work out who they are from.

1

GREETINGS!

IT'S SO BUSY IN THE OBSERVATORY. I PROGRAMMED MY COMPUTER TO GENERATE THIS LINE TO WISH YOU BON VOYAGE! MY NUBBLE SPACE TELESCOPE CHECKED THE ALIGNMENT OF THE STARS - THERE ARE STORMS AROUND TIKI TROPIC BUT THE REST OF THE ROUTE TO PIRATE PARADISE SHOULD BE PLAIN SAILING!

2

Dearest Bucky (I can call you that, can't I?),

When Roary told me that you were heading off on the seventy seas again I dashed down to The Port to wave goodbye. I assumed you'd want me to smash a bottle of vintage Toad Soda against the *Clipper*, cut a ribbon and pose for farewell photos, but by the time I got there you had GONE! I can only assume, sniff, that there was a technical hitch. Perhaps you'd like to explain when you're back in Port . . .

3

To my old pals Buck and Lefty,

I can't tell you how roarsome I think this new mission sounds! I haven't seen Pirate Paradise since I was a wee furry thing, holidaying with my Musky Huskies. Make sure that you fill the hold with as many treasures as you can find. There's always plenty of room for trinkets, charms and curiosities in the Bizarre Bazaar!

A. TYRA FANGS

C. TAMARA TESLA

B. BUSHY FANDANGO

Well blow me down and call me Barnacles, there be rogues in these parts! The *Clipper's* in spying distance of Cookie Crumb Canyon - shoulda known that Sweet Tooth would show up! That no-good lolly licker leaves a nasty taste in my mouth. Arrrrr!

Sweet Tooth's Hypno Blaster Cake Pops

Dr. Strangeglove's sugary sidekick never goes anywhere without a bulging bag of gobstoppers and a Hypno Blaster Lollipop. Sweet Tooth overindulges 24/7, but if you've eaten your Green today, give this scrummy recipe a try.

INGREDIENTS

- 1 shop bought basic chocolate sponge
- 1 450ml pot of vanilla buttercream icing
- 375g white chocolate chips
- Orange, pink and blue food colouring
- Pink and blue icing tubes
- Lollipop sticks
- A polystyrene block or cardboard box

Don't forget your toothbrush!

1 Ask an adult to gently slice the cake down the middle. Take each piece in your hand and rub the two halves together to crumble the sponge down.

2 Put your spongecake crumbs in a mixing bowl and spoon in the buttercream icing. Stir the mixture together until it forms a gooey dough.

3 Find a baking tray and line with a sheet of parchment.

4 Take out a generous dessertspoon of the creamy goo then use your hands to shape it into a neat ball. Put the ball on the baking sheet.

Did you know that these luv-erly lickable Hypno Blasters are actually bitesize cakes? When you've made a batch of these treats guard them carefully – Sweet Tooth is bound to sneak round to pilfer them!

5 Repeat step four, moulding as you go until you have filled the baking tray with evenly-shaped balls. Put the tray in the freezer and leave it for thirty minutes.

6 While the cake pops are chilling, ask an adult to help you melt the white chocolate chips. Tip the chips into a glass bowl and then set it on a pan of gently bubbling water. Make sure that the water doesn't touch the bowl. Stir the chips every so often until they are fully melted and then turn off the heat. Carefully separate your melted chocolate into three bowls and use the food colouring to make orange, pink and blue chocolate.

7 Take the cake pops out of the freezer and push a lolly stick into each one.

8 Dip the cake pops into your chosen coloured chocolate. You will need to work quickly so that the pops don't get too warm and gooey. If you run out of time, put them back in the freezer for a few minutes to firm up again.

9 Carefully balance your cake pop sticks upright until they set. Once set, you can use your icing tubes to decorate your your cake pops with a swirly pattern.

10 Pick out a cake pop and give it a taste test. Slurptastic!

You can stand your cake pops in an old block of polystyrene salvaged from a parcel or box. If you don't have one of these, ask an adult to score holes in an old cardboard box.

What's this? Don't forget the secret ingredient at the end! All my Hypno Blasters are dipped in a potent potion that sends Moshlings to sleep. Works a treat, too. Ha ha ha!!!

Buck's Beaches

Candy Cane Corals, Reggae Reef, Spraytona . . . **when it comes to beaches I've seen 'em all!** I love to string a hammock up between a couple of palm trees and rest me weary noggin. Here's a round-up of **the finest shores** this side of the Gulf Of New Gizmo.

THE SANDY DRAIN HOTEL PRIVATE BEACH, MUSIC ISLAND

If you've got a sackful of booty, charter a jet to Simon Growl's private airstrip on Music Island. It's the kind of mini-break only the most stellar Monsters can afford, hidden from prying paps on an über-exclusive stretch of sand! Order sunlounger service from the Sandy Drain Hotel and chill the day away sipping Essence of Blue and rubbing shoulders with your gooperstar friends.

MonSTAR rating ★ ★ ★ ★ ★
Zack Binspin says . . .

What a googeous beach! I can really kick back and let my mop flop!

BLEURGH BEACH

Crave that beach experience, but don't want to travel too far out of Monstro City? Bleurgh has it all! Surf dudes and sun-worshippers stomp here every weekend to play in the rockpools and make quick-sand castles. Acrobatic Seastars tumble and leap in the coral reefs – if you're lucky, one might even hitch a lift on your surfboard while you're riding the Potion Ocean waves.

MonSTAR rating ★ ★ ★ ★
Tyra Fangs says . . .

Bleurgh Beach is the perfect place to show-off my monstrous bikini collection. Love it!

GROAN BAY

Monsters on a budget will get a good deal down at Groan Bay – the prices are practically prehistoric! Head for Wailing Wharf, then look out for a jetty jutting into the blue. Slapstick Tortoises can't get enough of the place! You're bound to spot one practising fighting moves or flailing on the sand with its legs in the air.

MonSTAR rating ★ ★
Shelby says . . .

I come to Groan Bay every year to hibernate under the boardwalk. Hi-yaaa!

FRUIT FALLS

Foodies will love the nosh-pebbled waters of Fruit Falls! This beach is famous for its foamy tides and berry-strewn sands. Snozzle Wobbleson comes here to collect croakconuts to sell at the Gross-ery Store! Take a relaxing stroll or go Batty Bubblefish spotting. The Fishies float into land at low tide so they can loll and slurp in the sweet-scented foam.

MonSTAR rating ★ ★ ★ ★
Snozzle Wobbleson says . . .

If you stumble across a Batty Bubblefish, prepare to get glooped. It's gooily, gungily, goopendous!

AT THE ARCHIPELAGO

Cap'n Buck and his crew have loaded some **unbelievable masterpieces** onto the *Cloudy Cloth Clipper*. Sophisticated Monsters back home queue around the block to catch a glimpse of great artists like GRRRmeer, Fablo Fiasco and Groanet! Which works have the shipmates bagged today? **Draw a line to connect each piece to its proper title.**

Land ahoy! Lefty has spied the antique peaks of the Art Archipelago – a fine source of pirate treasure if ever there was one! Over the years I've **chanced upon all manner of great aaarrrrtwork** in these parts. I even once found the **rare Horrods Scream painting** languishing in a sunken chest in a far corner of the smallest island. Come on you scurvy lot, time to dock and fill your boots!

1

2

3

4

5

6

A ○ THE GREAT WAVE RIDER

D ○ GROANET'S ROTTER LILLIES

B ○ SCREAM

E ○ ROARHAL'S SOUP

C ○ POPPET WITH A PEARL EARRING

F ○ MONSTA LISA

19

Make Your Own Cloudy Cloth Clipper

YOU WILL NEED:

- **2 empty milk cartons**
  (Sour Milk is best, but any will do!)
- **Scissors**
- **Ruler**
- **Thin white card**
- **Sticky tape**
- **Pen**
- **Old newspapers**
- **Brown poster paint and brush**
- **Adhesive putty**
- **Felt-tipped pens**
- **Pencil**
- **Tracing paper**
- **Hole punch**
- **Three drinking straws**
- **Paper glue**

My *Cloudy Cloth Clipper* is the envy of Potion Ocean, make no mistake! She's got a majestic mizzenmast, roarsome riggin' and the poopiest poop deck ever seen by man or monster! So swashbucklers, **would you like to be making yourself a mini Clipper of yer own?** It won't cost you any doubloons, just a large helping of pirate know-how. Ready? Don't be lily-livered, **get crafting!**

1 Turn the first milk carton on its side. This will form the main body of your pirate ship.

2 Use your scissors and ruler to carefully cut out a piece of white card that you can wrap all the way around the bottom half of the milk carton. Stick the card in place using sticky tape.

3 At the back of the milk carton, tape another piece of card around the top. Trim it so that it is about 3cm higher than the edge of the carton. Put your pirate ship to one side for a moment.

4 Take the second milk carton and measure up 8cm from the bottom. Mark the line with a pen and then very carefully cut the base off at this point. The carton will be tricky to cut through, so you may be needing to ask an older shipmate to help you with this.

5 Use more tape to cover the base of this second carton with white card, so that you create a little white block. Use adhesive putty to stick the block onto the back of your model ship to form the upper deck.

6 Lay out some old newspaper and place your ship in the middle. Paint the ship from top to bottom with brown poster paint. Leave it to dry and then draw on portholes, doors and interesting wood details with a felt-tipped pen.

7 With a pencil, carefully pierce three holes in a row along the top of the upper deck. This will be the base for your masts.

8 Draw four sails and a flag onto plain white paper. Make sure that the flag design matches this picture. Decorate each piece with felt-tipped pens and cut it out.

9 Punch two holes into each of your sails and slide them onto drinking straws. Now push the straws into the holes in the upper deck. Make a short slit at the top of the middle straw.

10 Fold the flag in half and glue it together, then slide it onto the middle straw mast. Your *Cloudy Cloth Clipper* be ready! Arrrr!

Elder Furi says take care when using scissors! You'd be wise to heed his warning, too. The leader of the Super Moshis knows everything about ... everything!

21

A TRIP TO LONG GONE LAGOON

THE GLUNGE AGE

Back in those dim and distant times the moshisphere was a very different place. Everybody got around riding Ponies 'cos wheels hadn't been invented yet! Some strange species like Worldies hadn't even staggered into life. The monu-mental Moshlings spent their days standing about instead looking rather bored. In the Glunge Age, all the Birdies lived together in an ancient tree-village called Fluttertown. Legend has it that the dwelling is now submerged deep beneath Lake Inferior.

THE GREAT CUSTARD FLOOD OF 99999.5

How important was this gungy custard catastrophe? It's only THE most devastating occurrence in Monstro City history! Very few monsters can remember firsthand the day that Mount Eggiecrest erupted, spilling yellow ooze in all directions. It glooped into the ocean! It gunged into the valleys! The custardy stuff even slimed its way through the streets, smothering everything in its icky sticky path. Even though the Great Flood happened oodles of years ago, every Moshi history book records the date in big letters. If it wasn't for hardworking Titchy Trundlebots turning up to rebuild the place, Monstro City would still be a soggy custard swamp today.

BABY BUCK

Shiver me timbers! That'd be me on my very first birthday, many, many, MANY moon-sters ago! What a hairily handsome buccaneer in the making I was too! I were born into the enormous Curl-footed Bearded Barnacle family, proud son of Bernie and Barry Barnacle.

Baby Buck's 1st Birthday!

Land ahoy! Screw up the charts, draw a new map – looks like we've happened upon an **undiscovered land*** ! Valley Mermaids bobbing about these parts say this shore is called '**Long Gone Lagoon**', **a mysterious place** where sailors get transported back in time. Hmmm . . . If we're going back in time, I wonder if I can have lunch again? Me belly could do with second helpings! Here we go – better **record everythin' in me captain's log book, just in case . . .**

ELDER FURI'S SUPER MOSHIVERSITY DAYS

I knew I had gone way, way back when I encountered Elder Furi as a wee Monster! The bright-eyed young critter hadn't even grown his beard yet! On his very first day, Younger Furi (as he was known back then) made a mysterious new mate called Lavender Troggs. My canny pirate sense sniffs something dodgy about this student. No good will come of that Troggsy critter, mark my words!

BUSTER BUMBLECHOPS' EARLY EXPLORATIONS

Rusty cutlasses! There be Buster Bumblechops in his research ship, *Windingo II*, circling the volcanic island of Emberbooze. The last time that vessel was on the water must be nigh on fifty years ago. Sadly I heard tell that this expedition came to a sticky end. Buster had just met up with Burnie the Fiery Frazzledragon when the Beastie belched and set fire to the *Windingo's* sails! I voyaged past its shipwreck only the other week . . .

Avast, I won't be forgetting me time at Long Gone Lagoon. The sun is setting – best get the *Cloudy Cloth Clipper* back on the water before we become 'Long Gone', too!

*Well it definitely wasn't there earlier and that be a pirate fact!

SINK ME, Bucko, there be a squall up ahead! Hoist the mainsail and batten down the hatches! ALL PAWS ON DECK!

SEVENTY STORMY SEAS

Only a bold (or excessively daft) band of buccaneers would be willing to plot a course around **Tiki Tropic**, five leagues south of the Cape of Gloop Hope. The **perilous waves are more dangerous** here than the Bear-muda Triangle!

Study this snap of the *Cloudy Cloth Clipper* taking its chances through the very eye of the storm. Lefty, Peppy and Hansel are all working hard on deck, but **who else can you spy?** Yep, you're not seeing things dear reader, **there are stowaways on board!**

There are eight of the rascals hiding all over the ship. Write each of their names in the list below.

1. ....
2. ....
3. ....
4. ....
5. ....
6. ....
7. ....
8. ....

Most Wanted

You could knock the Cap'n over with a feather when he discovers **Buster Bumblechops** hiding on the poop deck! The Moshling expert wants to join the voyage and **see what new critters he can spy.** Buster's heard that there's all sorts of weird and wonderful species roaming these parts.

Check out my field notes. Fangtastic stuff, eh? I just can't wait to see what my expedition will turn up next. Happy huntin' Moshling fans!

19
ULTRA RARE

Name and Species:
Shoney the Amazin' Blazin' Raisin

Mini Bio

Great balls of fire? Not quite because these fiery fruit-based critters are actually Moshlings. Notorious for accidentally setting things on fire as they whoosh through Monstro City at breakneck speeds, Amazin' Blazin' Raisins are thought to ignite and take flight whenever they hear the phrase 'shrivelled grapes'. Twisted firestarters? You bet!

49
UNCOMMON

Name and Species:
Lurgee the Sniffly Splurgee

Mini Bio

Please wash your hands, Sniffly Splurgees are highly infectious – in a good way, because despite the constant coughs and sniffles these friendly, bacteria-loving Moshlings soak up germs and viruses, keeping the world of Moshi bug-free. In fact the only downside to owning a Sniffly Splurgee is that they stink of cough syrup. Yuck!

119
COMMON

Name and Species:
Topsy Turvy the Tardy Timer

Mini Bio

Time waits for no Moshi, especially Tardy Timers because they are always running late. And that's weird because the powdered egg running through their hourglass figures is rumoured to tickle their tummies whenever they are delayed. Then again, you'd probably be late too if you spent all day doing handstands yelling, 'Ooh, it tickles!'

Name and Species:
Peekaboo the Oakey-Dokey Hokey-Pokey

31 UNCOMMON

Mini Bio
Is it a walking tree stump or a shy woodland critter in disguise? Who knows, because Oakey-Dokey Hokey-Pokies scurry away whenever you get near them. One thing's for sure, these highly-strung Moshlings will squirt slippy sap at anyone who tickles so much as a twig, so leaf 'em alone!

Name and Species:
Sprinkles the Magical Tinkler

42 COMMON

Mini Bio
They might look like jolly watering cans but these big-nozzled Moshlings sprinkle more than mere water. Tickle their tootsies and a kaleidoscopic shower of magical tinkles will cover everything within a three Moshimetre radius, spreading joy and happiness. Magical Tinklers can even toot tunes, leading some experts to believe they are related to Silly Snufflers.

Name and Species:
Ziggy the Quirky Koala

26 UNCOMMON

Mini Bio
Pump up the glam because Quirky Koalas are the music-loving Moshlings that enjoy face-painting and stomping around to flamboyant old songs. If you see one sprinkling glitter on the ground, don't worry – it's probably preparing to mark its territory by performing a signature glitter angel.

Name and Species:
Hissy the Jazzy Wiggler

22 RARE

Mini Bio
'Psst . . .' No, it's not a secret, it's the noise Jazzy Wigglers make whenever they hear a wild tune. Distant relatives of Beatnik Boas, these way-cool Moshlings can't resist making jazzy sounds 24/7 by poking out their tongues and shaking their jellybean tail rattles. Put simply, they don't wanna hiss a thing!

I Spy Candy Shoals

Our voyage sails on past the scrumptastic shores of the Candy Shoals. Whenever I visit delicious destinations like this, **I always take a picture.** I'd have a good album by now **if pesky Moshlings didn't keep leaping into the background!**

Poor Cap'n Buck has been photobombed more times than he cares to remember! Flick through the pirate's potty holiday snaps. Cheeky critters have jumped into the shots at the very last second! **Can you spy the Moshlings hiding in the background? List the names** of the imposters underneath each sugary snap.

1. CANDY CANE CAVERNS

PHOTOBOMBED BY:

....

....

....

2. CANDY SHOALS

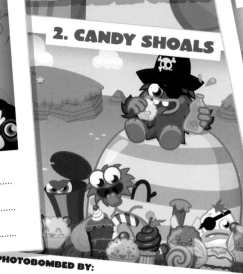

PHOTOBOMBED BY:

....

....

....

3. KNICKERBOCKER NOOK

PHOTOBOMBED BY:

....

....

....

4. RAMEKIN PLAIN

PHOTOBOMBED BY:

....

....

....

5. CHILLYBOT STATE PARK

PHOTOBOMBED BY:

....

....

....

28

BUCK'S BUCKET LIST

Ah me hearties, I've roamed the seventy seas for more years than I care to remember! I've seen the gleaming lights of Cadabra Flash, the city sights of Goo York, and everything in between. **You name it, I've crossed it off my chart!** So where be my **top five dream destinations?** Here's Buck's **booty-licious bucket list...**

1. Lush Lagoon

Why? This be my ultimate holiday destination. Coconut-hair hammocks, swaying palm trees and lots of loot – what's not to love?!

2. The Barmy Swami Jungle

Why? Rare thumpkin seeds grow in these parts. The inka-inka juice sloshing around inside each one is a prized pirate commodity!

3. Jollywood

Why? Who doesn't dream of going to Jollywood some day? I bet I'd have gooperstars fighting to play me in Buck: The Movie.

4. Fang-Ten Valley

Why? Squidge tells me that the Crazy Caves here have twinkly Rox lying about for anyone to help themselves. Sounds good to me!

5. The Taki Taki Islands

Why? Disco Duckies are always raving about this cool gaggle of islands in the middle of Lake Neon Soup. Sounds quackers to me!

Bubblebath Bay

Buck's right-hand Monster Lefty has **scribbled some drawings of Bubblebath Bath** into his scurvy sketchbook – not bad, eh? **Study the artist's impression** at the top, then **compare** it to the picture at the bottom. Can you find **eight differences between them?**

A

B

'I'm forever blowing bubbles, pretty bubbles in the air!' Being a soap-dodger (all pirates loathe soap), Bubblebath Bay 'ain't me favourite place to drop anchor. The shores are cluttered with fancy rubber ducks and rubbery-rough loofah grass! That's not all – Shampoo Lagoon to the south of the isle has a conditioner current that is totally treacherous. Nah, I be happy to peer at the place through my spyglass and Keep on sailing!

> What's this I've found, floating in the drink? 'Tis a **message in the bottle, signed by Elder Furi**, no less! The entire note has been **written in code!** The beardily brilliant old monster only writes secret messages when there be scallywags about. All hands on deck, we need to **get this code cracked!**

Calling all Super Moshis! Can you crack this curious code?
Every letter is represented by a number, but some of the digits have been washed away. Use your pirate powers of deduction to **complete the codekey, then get deciphering!**

Elder Furi

A	B	C	D	E	F	G	H	I	J	K	L	M	N	O	P	Q	R	S	T	U	V	W	X	Y	Z

Land ahoy! I spy Futuristic Falls!

31

DR STRANGEGLOVE
versus Elder Furi

Buck's adventure in Futuristic Falls has revealed something sinister – there's a diabolical plan to bring darkness to Monstro City! Only Elder Furi, and you can put a stop to Dr. Strangeglove and his crazy C.L.O.N.C. minions. It's time to read the **SEASON 2** mission log and hone your Super Moshi skills!

MISSION SM 1

CLOSE ENCOUNTERS OF THE ZOSHI KIND

The Super Moshis need to investigate the UFO crash site on Music Island, but you can't do it alone. Joining forces with Buster Bumblechops leads you deep into the Unknown Zone!

Which rather sunburnt Monster poses for the camera at the end of the Mission 1 trailer?

SANDY DRAIN SHENANIGANS

MISSION SM 2

The exclusive Sandy Drain Hotel is under the moo-dy new management of Frau Now BrownKau. Can you outsmart the fearsome Frau and locate Captain Squirk's Zoshling deputy?

Which Zoshling do you meet in this mission?

MISSION SM 3

BUNGLE IN THE JUNGLE

The Gombala Gombala jungle is alive with Hoodoo hijinks! Could Chief Big Bad Bill and his pals hold the key to helping the Zoshlings get home? Super Moshis must find the ingredients for a potent Hoodoo Strew!

Which ex-C.L.O.N.C. members do you encounter in Snaggle Tooth Swamp?

BIG TOP BALLY-HOO

MISSION SM 4

Captain Squirk needs you to enter the Cirque du Bonbon and find one of his missing crew. Can you get through the freaky funfair and outsmart Sweet Tooth?

What is the name of the strange, rotund creatures that work at the circus?

CIRQUE DU BONBON

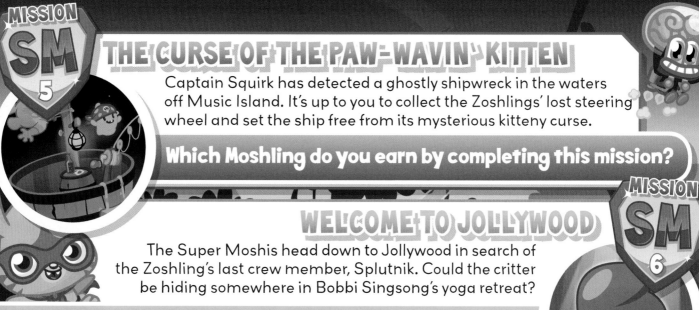

MISSION SM 5
THE CURSE OF THE PAW-WAVIN' KITTEN

Captain Squirk has detected a ghostly shipwreck in the waters off Music Island. It's up to you to collect the Zoshlings' lost steering wheel and set the ship free from its mysterious kitteny curse.

Which Moshling do you earn by completing this mission?

MISSION SM 6
WELCOME TO JOLLYWOOD

The Super Moshis head down to Jollywood in search of the Zoshling's last crew member, Splutnik. Could the critter be hiding somewhere in Bobbi Singsong's yoga retreat?

Which new villain shows his face in Welcome to Jollywood?

MISSION SM 7
MASTERS OF THE SWOONIVERSE

Prepare for blast-off as you boldly go where no Moshi has gone before – outer space! The Zoshling's ship, *Rhapsody 2*, is standing by and the final countdown has started.

Which uninvited guest takes control of the ship during this mission?

MISSION SM 8
KICK SOME ASTEROID

When your escape pod crashes on an asteroid, you need to get outta there fast. Can you team up with Wally Warpspeed, Fizzy and Rover to get the pod back on course?

What is Wally Warpspeed's job?

MISSION SM 9
MISSING ON A STAR

On a C.L.O.N.C. space base far, far away the Zoshlings have been captured! You and the rest of the Super Moshis must lead the operation to set them free and put a stop to C.L.O.N.C.'s wicked plans.

Which game show do you enter in this mission?

MISSION SM 10
COSMIC COUNTDOWN

It's the final countdown. Only you and the Super Moshis can defeat C.L.O.N.C. and save the world from total meltdown!

Which Moshi mountain begins to melt in this final encounter?

Cap'n Buck and his crew have found the fabled Futuristic Falls, but . . .

Correct, Captain Cloth-ears! Using the technology of the future I will invade the past . . .

Dr. Strangeglove has beaten us to it! And he's got an arrr-my of robotic rascals!

" I will take my robots back in time and seize control of Monstro City – and then the entire Moshi-Sphere! "

MONSTRO City

We'd better be gettin' away from Futuristic Falls an' back to the past! Raise the sails!

WHOOSH!

Puzzling Pieces Of Eight

Onwards scurvy pirate pals, Pirate Paradise lies up ahead! Tamara Tesla and Prof. Purplex visited this far-off isle for their holidays last year. It's got crossword coves, word search shores and a mind-boggling myriad of mountainous mazes.

Spy Glass

Take a peek through the Captain's telescope. Who can you spy out there floating aimlessly on the seventy seas? Name the marooned Moshling, then scribble their species underneath.

....

(..................................)

NIFTY SHIFTY

Cap'n Buck booty quest often takes him to scorching hot tropical islands. What does he put on his fur to protect it from sunburn? Move each letter of the alphabet forward one space to find out!

FQNVKND UDQZ FDK

____ ____ ____

A   B   C

D   E   F

Odd Cuddly Out

Awww . . . look at this cute shelf of Cuddly Pirates! Buck and his crew all love 'em, but has there been a stitch-up? Study the pirate toys, then circle the one that doesn't quite match up to the rest.

Pirate Patter

Across

1. The look-out point at the top of the tallest mast.
2. What pirates say when they greet each other.
3. The lowest, stinkiest part of the ship.
4. Pirate nosh.
5. The thing that punished sailors have to walk off.

Down

1. A sharp, curved sword.
2. To wash or mop.
3. The top floor on a pirate galleon.
4. Pirate treasure.
5. The left side of a ship.

Marine Mix-up

Unscramble the names of these watery wonders.

ILGA

– – – –

UBRPL

– – – – –

TEMLRY

– – – – – –

LETSYAN

– – – – – – –

CAVE COUNTING

This secret cave has turquoise waters and Rox-encrusted walls – it's totally far out! Peer into the soggy chamber. How many sassy Valley Mermaids can you count gossiping inside?

39

MUSIC ISLAND MEDLEY

Arrrggh, after that brain-melting mooch around Puzzle Paradise, I be glad to be moving on! Barnacles aren't made to solve sums and crack conundrums from breakfast to bedtime. Now the compass is set for our next stop. The *Cloudy Cloth Clipper* can't pass Music Island without weighing anchor for a day or two. Come on me hearties, it'll be roarsome!

THE SANDY DRAIN HOTEL

The super-luxe hotel is for Moshi megastars only. It's got everything – a private beach, a gourmet restaurant, spa huts and a totally roarsome guitar-shaped pool. Check in and chill out!

THE UNKNOWN ZONE

No two ways about it, there's something seriously strange going on in the heart of Music Island! The Unknown Zone has been befuddling fuddlers ever since it was revealed as a UFO crash site. Could there really be Zoshlings in these parts?

GOMBALA GOMBALA JUNGLE

If limbo's your thing, sashay inland to meet Big Bad Bill. His rare Woolly Blue Hoodoo tribe live in the remote Gombala Gombala Jungle, playing bongos and drinking OoblaDoobla juice out of coconut shells.

Buster Bumblechops' jungle survival tips

1. Do eat the purple bananas - they're scumptidiliumptious!

2. Don't eat the yellow ones - they're sour as rotten lemons, trust me!

3. Do look out for the graceful moonlit gazelles. The wildlife is superb in these parts.

4. Don't forget to check your boots for creepy crawlies every morning. The local spiders like to snuggle up in your socks.

5. Do enjoy the distant jungle rumbles of Mount Krakka Blowa.

6. Don't stick around if the rumbles get any louder. She could blow at any moment!

JOLLYWOOD

GOOEY GALLEON

Shiver me timbers! There's something strange about the shipwreck lodged in the rocks off Music Island. The timbers creak, the sails billow and piratey figures cackle in the night air. Go there if you dare!

THE CIRQUE DU MOSHI

Roll-up, roll-up, roll-up, the circus has come to town. Buy a bucket of Slopcorn, try your luck at the Quack Attack stand, then step into the big top. It's the greatest show on earth!

Scare Force One

A strange shadow has drifted over Music Island and I don't like it one itty, bitty bit! That blimp has blocked my light too many times before. The confounded cloud-bumper has got to be **Dr. Strangeglove's** airship - *Scare Force One!*

Scare Force One makes a glumptasmic sight! **Use the colour key** to bring the blimp to life in shady purples, gloomy blues and devious greens.

C.L.O.N.C.
COLOUR KEY:

- 1 = Dark Purple
- 2 = Light Purple
- 3 = Blue
- 4 = Green
- 5 = Yellow
- 6 = Orange

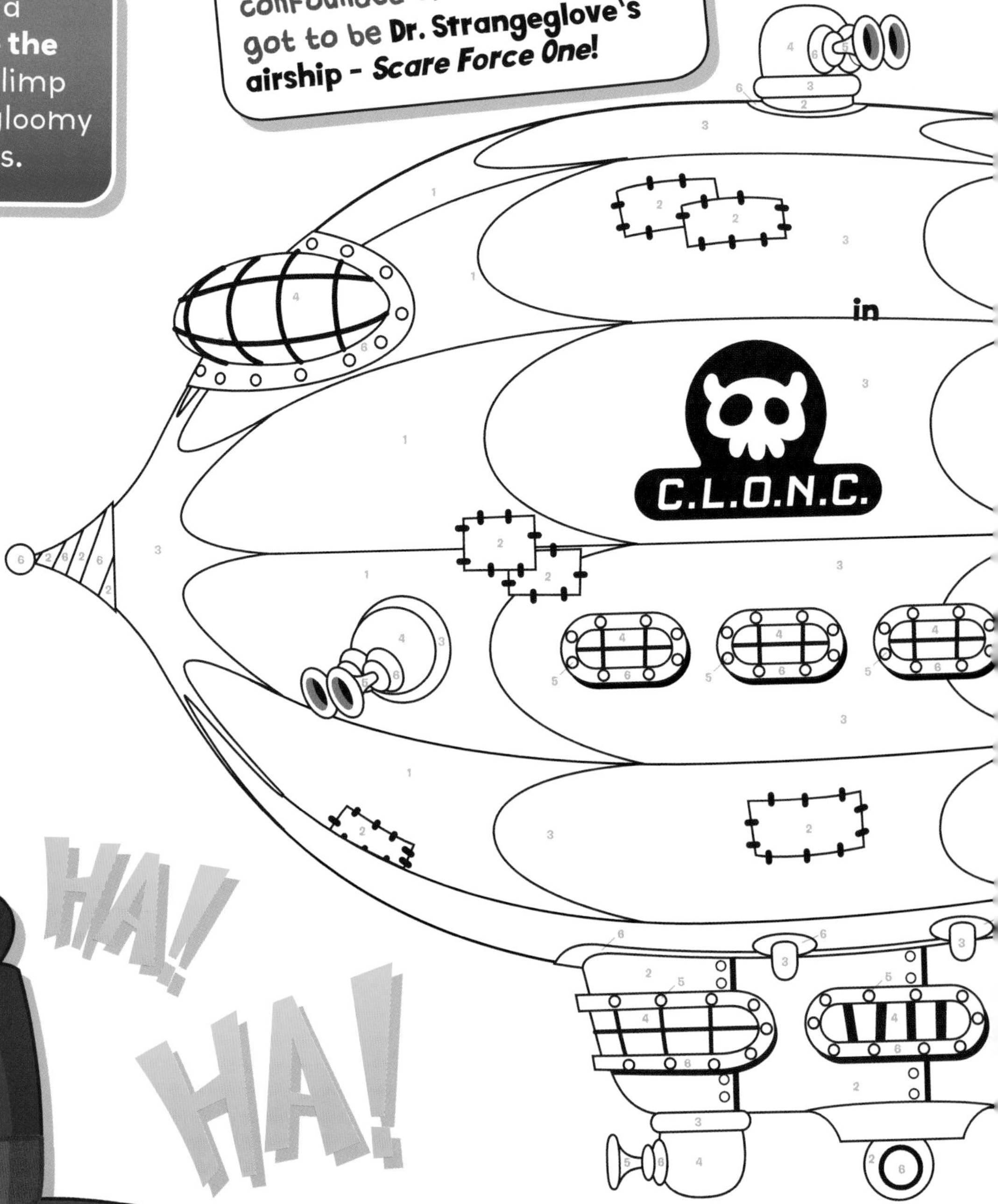

C.L.O.N.C.

in

HA! HA! HA! HA! MWAAAAH!

Time to give that
landlubbing scoundrel
the slip, methinks!

43

The Devious Dr.'s Periscope

Some people never give up! If you're thinking of joining the Criminal League of Naughty Critters this make-it might just be for you. The Dr.'s periscope uses a wickedly clever combination of mirrors to see around bends, peep over walls and sneak under tables! Despicable!

Pssst! While Buck is having his fur frou-froued at the Sandy Drain spa, I wanted to show you this! My latest invention is an utterly devious, deliciously underhand piece of spying kit. No C.L.O.N.C. agent should leave the house without one! The villainous uses are endless! Be afraid, pesky pirates, be very afraid . . .

YOU WILL NEED:

- **2 empty tall 1 litre juice cartons**
- **2 small pocket mirrors** (the ones found in old make-up containers are fangtastic!)
- **Sticky tape**
- **Marker pen**
- **Ruler**
- **Old newspapers**
- **Poster paints and brush**

1 Wash both juice cartons out and turn them upside down to dry. Pull the tabs to completely open up the top of each carton.

2 Slide one of the open ends of one carton into the other one. Use sticky tape to stick the cartons together, creating one long box.

3 With your marker pen and ruler, draw a 5cm x 5cm window at the bottom of the front of the box. Flip the cartons over and draw one about the same size at the top of the back.

4 Ask an adult to help you pierce through the cartons and cut both windows out.

5 Lay out some old newspaper and get out your paints. Use a brush to paint your periscope all over in your favourite design.

Periscopes are for sneaking around, so think about when you might use it! If you're planning to take it to the park, try painting it in greens and browns so it is disguised from goody-goodies. If you fancy night-snooping around the house, choose dark purples and black instead.

6 When your periscope has dried out, lay it on its side with the bottom window facing to the right. On the top left edge of the carton measure 7cm up from the bottom and make a small mark. Now use the ruler to draw a diagonal line from the mark to the bottom right corner. This diagonal line is angle that your mirrors need to sit at.

7 Ask your adult helper to very carefully cut from the bottom corner up the diagonal line. Only cut the same length as the depth of your mirror.

8 Slide the first mirror in through the slit in the carton and tape it in place.

9 Flip the periscope over and repeat steps 6 to 8 with the second mirror.

10 Once your mirrors are in place, it's time to get snooping! Your periscope will let you peep round corners without showing yourself, look over walls that are taller than you and pry under tables without getting on your hands and knees. Mwaah Haa-Haa!

The HateKeeper says beware of sharp scissors! Ask an adult to help with cutting out the cartons. Even Sinister Ministers need to call in the big guys from time to time.

I EVIL

THERE BE ZOSHLINGS!

HOW MUCH DO YOU KNOW ABOUT THE MYSTERIOUS ZOSHLINGS? HAVE YOU MET THEM IN THE SERIES 2 MISSIONS YET? GIVE A SPACE-AGE SALUTE TO CAPTAIN SQUIRK AND THE CREW OF THE *RHAPSODY 2*.

I was wanderin' back to me trusty galleon when **Lefty spotted something curious** coming out of the Unknown Zone. **A plume of smoke** was snaking its way up towards the sky, bold as you like! Before you could say 'Barbecued Bubblefish', my stowaway **Buster was off to investigate,** muttering some bunkum about a new breed of Moshlings. That be the moment that I first **met the Zoshlings** – a merry crew **from the planet Symphonia.** A merry old time we had too, swapping songs and glugging cosmic gloop!

CAPTAIN SQUIRK

The *Rhapsody 2's* **heroic captain** is a Zoshling with a mission. Captain Squirk roams the Swooniverse exploring new worlds, **seeking out quirky new melodies** and voyaging where no Zoshling has ever voyaged before. As well as being a **first-rate leader,** the alien is also out of this world at playing marvellous melodies on the spoons.

FIRST OFFICER OOZE

Every great leader needs a **right hand alien** to turn to and Captain Squirk is no exception. First Officer Ooze may be a **little slow at slithering** from A to B, **but the cosmic gloop he can generate is second to none!** As well as using the icky stuff to oil the computers aboard the *Rhapsody 2*, the gloop also has magical tuning properties. Just one teaspoon can turn the most raucous Roarker into a musical gooperstar!

SPLUTNIK

This **bubble-brained alien** was recruited when he was still just a space cadet to serve as the *Rhapsody 2's* **ingenious chief engineer.** As well as being **über-techy** (Tamara Tesla would love to invite him to her lab), Splutnik is a **fangtastically-talented kazoo player!** He is also very proud to show visitors how his jetpack can get him from one side of the Silky Way to the other in less than twelve argh-secs.

DR. C FINGZ

Any alien feeling queasy aboard ship is immediately dispatched to Dr. C Fingz's Sick Bay. **The chief medical officer** is a whiz at bandaging up battered Zoshlings and flushing out space bugs. The insightful scientist has a **telepathic wiggle-stalk that he uses to read alien minds,** allowing him to communicate with weird and wacky life-forms right across the Swooniverse. Far out!

It's life, Lefty, but not as we know it!

CAPTAIN CODSWALLOP'S CROSSWORD

Captain Buck's ocean instincts are right yet again! The wreck is the cursed *Gooey Galleon*. The skipper, Captain Codswallop, has set you a challenge. He's started filling the letters into this **crossword puzzle**, but **can you finish it off?** Use the picture clues to help you.

Music Island had one more surprise up its cheeky sleeve. A salty night breeze blew the *Cloudy Cloth Clipper* within a skeeter's splash of an old shipwreck rocking off the east coast. I could have sworn **I saw a light glinting** from the Captain's Cabin. **There be ghostly goings on there**, or I'll be a salsa-ing seagull.

8. CAPTAIN CODSWALLOP

ACROSS

2. _ _ _ _ _

3. _ _ _ _ _ _

7. _ _ _ _ _ _

8. CAPTAIN CODSWALLOP

9. _ _ _ _ _ _

10. _ _ _ _ _ _

DOWN

1. _ _ _ _ _ _ _ _ _ _

2. _ _ _ _ _ _

4. _ _ _ _

5. _ _ _ _ _

6. _ _ _ _ _ _

FIND THE FISHY

Potion Ocean be so calm tonight, I couldn't resist diving into the drink! **I love swimming** down to the **murky depths and seeing what I can spy.** Last time I dipped me fur in the water, there was my long-lost uncle Blake Barnacle clinging on a rock!

Study the soggy scene, ticking off the Fishies said to be living in these parts as you find it.

Can you find...?

5 Acrobatic SeaStars

4 Batty Bubblefish

3 Songful Seahorses

1 Valley Mermaid

...and Octopeg

Into The Gulf Of New Gizmo

These sparky shores have given **Sprockett and Hubbs** the inspiration to **start inventing again!** What will the crazies come up with next? The latest offering from S&H industries is in your hands. **Fill the blueprint with the most ingenious invention ever.**

No two days are the same when you're aboard the *Cloudy Cloth Clipper*, all me crew agree! Today we drifted into the Gulf of New Gizmo, but to tell you the truth I don't fancy staying too long. **Everything here be electrified!** When I leant against one of the local Powergranate Trees, I got zapped on me back! **Totally shocking if you ask me.**

Potty Times On Potion Ocean

Nights on Potion Ocean can get boring me hearties, if you're stuck in your cabin all on yer ownsome. Me and my shipmates gather in the galley instead. We have a fine old time every evening, swilling Snail Ale and telling salty sea tales. Me and Lefty take turns spinning yarns and singing along to the squeezebox. Dash my buttons, we do have a roar-cous time of it!

Can you tell a tale to keep Buck and his company amused this evening? **The Captain has started a story**, but he needs a bright young sailor to **decide what happens next.** Use your pens and pencils to write a gripping yarn, **then draw pictures** in the frames. Don't forget to use lots of piratey words!

Monstrously early one morning, Lefty banged on me cabin door.

"Wake up, Buck!" he hollered. "You gotta see this ...!"

I leapt out me hammock so fast I walloped me noggin on the cabin ceiling. "Arrrrrrr!" I groaned, reaching for me eye patch and captain's hat. I tucked me spyglass under me arm and staggered out on deck. Outside a curling, swirling fog curled and swirled all around the ship. I clambered up the ropes and peered out to sea.

"Bah!" I spluttered, "I've seen fog a thousand times. That ain't worth waking me up from me beauty sleep!"

Lefty shook his tentacles.

"It's not the fog," he muttered, "or anything out on the drink. Take a peek on your cabin door."

"Well I'll be ..."

There on me own door, for any Monster to see, was a piece of parchment skewered by a dagger! I marched up and tore it down.

Hansel, Squidge and the rest of the crew gathered round, their little Moshling faces filled with horror.

"There's nothing on it," whispered Lefty, "apart from ... apart from ..." Lefty's voice trailed into silence. The parchment

Who's threatened Cap'n Buck? Be it smugglers? C.L.O.N.C. agents? Or something even more 'orrible ...?

Make your tale as thrilling as you can, hearties! Pirates love to be s-s-s-cared!

was blank apart from a great, black spot ⬛ slap-bang in the centre! In the pirate world, that can only mean one thing. "Mateys," I said solemnly. "The *Cloudy Cloth Clipper* has received a threat of the lowest order. Someone be out to get us!"

. . . The End Aharrrrrrrrrrrrr!!!!!!

Pirate X Paradise

Booty Clues

1. Head south 4 squares, and then east 4 squares to Blockhead Butte.

2. Hop across the bridge to the mainland, then walk 5 squares north.

3. Step 2 squares east, then 4 squares south.

4. Look east across Soprano Sahara, and head for the cactus by the bridge.

5. Cross the bridge. Move 1 square south, 2 squares east and 2 squares south.

Reckon you're within grabbing distance of Buck's booty? Draw a bold X on the spot.

Golden Gu

The Golden Swamp

Blockhead Butte

START

Shipwreck

Paradise Lagoon

Flag falls

DRINKS

Barnacle Bay

rano Sahara

Plank Peak

Sunken Treasure

N
W   E
S

The Duster of Destiny

Aha, me hearties, I be one happy pirate! I found me treasure, felt the sea air blowing through me beard and had a rollicking adventure along the way. It's time for the *Cloudy Cloth Clipper* to return to The Port. I got to unload me booty and prepare for me next voyage! Where will I be heading off to next, you ask? That's up for the Duster of Destiny to decide! Smooth sailing matey. Arrrgghh!

Monstro City is a-buzz with Buck's return! The *Cloudy Cloth Clipper* is **front page news.** All Moshis have one thing on their mind. **What will Buck get up to now?** This mystic quiz might give you some clues, but then again, it might not – **the Duster of Destiny is hugely unpredictable!** Have fun anyway working through this trippy tick test. Can you triumph with ten out of ten?

1. What is the name of this unpredictable Moshling?
A. Furnando the Mystic Moggie ☐
B. Furprendo the Mystic Mister ☐
C. Purrdando the Messy Moggy ☐

2. Tamara Tesla is already busy plotting out a new course for Buck. Where does she work?
A. In the Candy Cane Caverns ☐
B. In a back room at the En-Gen plant ☐
C. In the Observatory beside the Port ☐

3. While he's on dry land, Buck fancies paying a visit to his old pals Pete and Lila. Where can he find them?
A. Ooh La Lane ☐
B. Gift Island ☐
C. Main Street ☐

4. One of the *Daily Growl* staff reckons they can predict Buck's fortune. Who is it?
A. Roary Scrawl ☐
B. Agony Ant ☐
C. Ruby Scribblez ☐

5. Lefty fancies visiting somewhere spooky next. Where might be a good place to start?

A. Goosebump Manor

B. Bleurgh Beach

C. Ice-Scream Store

6. For his next trip, Buck wants to recruit a cheerful Moshling to keep the crew in a good mood. Who would be the best choice?

A. Flumpy

B. Tomba

C. Pocito

7. The owner of Yukea has asked Buck to bring some piratey furniture back from his next voyage. What is his name?

A. Sly Chance

B. Moe Yukky

C. Gilbert Finnster

8. Which Lucky can bring Buck good fortune with a single wave of its paw?

A. Tingaling

B. O'Really

C. Penny

9. Buster Bumblechops has asked if his assistant can jump aboard for the *Clipper's* next trip. What is his sidekick called?

A. Huffy Snookums

B. Tuffy Wookums

C. Snuffy Hookums

10. Elder Furi has a Super Moshi mission he'd like Buck to consider. Who guards the door to his Volcano HQ?

A. Rocky the Baby Blockhead

B. The Gatekeeper

C. Rickety Boo

Answers

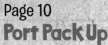

Page 10
Port Pack Up

A	D	J	S	S	A	L	G	Y	P	S	R	Y	X	E
C	R	O	A	K	C	O	N	U	T	J	U	I	C	E
C	X	I	U	U	B	S	Q	U	X	V	B	E	H	M
U	P	X	G	L	Z	N	M	W	O	T	B	X	G	J
D	W	I	Q	L	K	A	R	G	B	K	E	L	X	N
D	Z	M	D	A	B	P	N	I	X	B	R	A	S	R
L	G	N	F	N	P	P	X	A	Q	Q	F	O	V	V
Y	Q	H	W	D	D	E	R	V	R	Z	U	H	I	Y
P	A	S	H	B	B	R	G	D	Y	P	C	K	T	Z
I	E	I	C	O	N	R	H	O	H	N	K	S	A	A
R	N	F	M	N	E	F	C	O	A	L	S	W	Z	C
A	J	Y	K	E	P	C	W	K	M	G	F	P	Q	J
T	U	I	N	S	T	I	U	S	G	N	I	V	I	D
E	T	E	N	T	A	C	L	E	C	H	A	I	R	E

Page 11
Dr. Strangeglove Will See You Now . . .
The Doctor will see you now . . . Mwah-ah-ah-ah-ah-aaa!
Sneaky, sly and shifty, let me introduce myself
I'm the doctor they call **Strangeglove**, a hazard to your health!
I'm here to wreak some mayhem with my terrifying schemes,
And glump your silly **Moshlings** with my dastardly machines!

Glump chorus
Strangeglove, Strangeglove, they call him Dr. Strangeglove,
Strangeglove, Strangeglove, the one to be afraid of!
Strangeglove, Strangeglove, they call him Dr. Strangeglove,
Strangeglove, Strangeglove, Strangeglove, Strange

I assume you think it's sinister to hold an ancient grudge
But understand it cost my **hand**, so don't be quick to judge
A **Musky Husky** mangled it and chewed it like a shoe
He thought it was some **sausages** so now this **glove** must do
Don't impede my evil deeds or try to foil my plans
Even though I wear this **glove** I have some helping hands
So peek outside your **window** and check behind the **door**
Is Dr. **Strangeglove** lurking or has he called before?

Glump chorus

Let's 'em have it, **Fishlips**!
Blow harder, you spherical fool!
I'll show those **Super Moshis**
Oh yes, nasty!
Today Monstro City, tomorrow . . .
the world, the WORLD!!!

Page 15
Postcards From Monstro City
A - 2 / B - 3 / C - 1

Page 19
At The Archipelago
1 - D   2 - F   3 - C   4 - A   5 - E   6 - B

Pages 24-25
Seventy Stormy Seas
1. Buster Bumblechops
2. Snuffy Hookums
3. Diavlo
4. Katsuma
5. Bushy Fandango
6. Scamp
7. Big Bad Bill
8. Coolio.

Page 28
I Spy Candy Shoals
1. Purdy, Honey and McNulty
2. I.G.G.Y., Dr. Strangelove and Pirate Pong
3. Coolio, Gracie and Leo,
4. Tiamo, Betty and Cutie Pie
5. General Fuzuki, Sooki-Yaki and Roxy

Page 30
Bubblebath Bay

Page 31
Message In A Bottle
BE ON YOUR GUARD, BUCK – DANGER LIES AHEAD!
DR. STRANGEGLOVE IS FOLLOWING THE CLOUDY CLOTH
CLIPPER. DON'T LET C.L.O.N.C. MAKE YOU WALK THE PLANK!
Elder Furi: Key:

A	B	C	D	E	F	G	H	I
26	6	16	7	15	9	5	24	8

J	K	L	M	N	O	P	Q	R
4	14	1	19	12	18	11	20	25

S	T	U	V	W	X	Y	Z
23	22	3	13	2	17	10	21

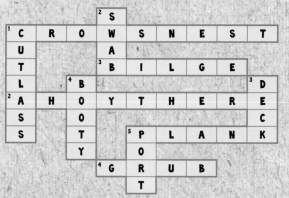

Pages 34-35

Dr. Strangeglove versus Elder Furi

Mission 1: **CLOSE ENCOUNTERS OF THE ZOSHI KIND**
Bubba

Mission 2: **SANDY DRAIN SHENANIGANS**
First Officer Ooze

Mission 3: **BUNGLE IN THE JUNGLE**
Sprockett and Tubbs

Mission 4: **BIG TOP BALLY-HOO**
Clumps

Mission 5: **THE CURSE OF THE PAW-WAVIN' KITTEN**
Tingaling

Mission 6: **WELCOME TO JOLLYWOOD**
Big Chief Tiny Head

Mission 7: **MASTERS OF THE SWOONIVERSE**
Dr. Strangeglove

Mission 8: **KICK SOME ASTEROID**
Wally is a Cosmic Rox miner

Mission 9: **MISSING ON A STAR**
Squeal of Fortune

Mission 10: **COSMIC COUNTDOWN**
Mount Silimanjaro

Pages 38-39

Puzzling Pieces Of Eight

Spy Glass
It's Snookums the Baby Tumteedum

Nifty Shifty
GROWLOE VERA GEL

Odd Cuddly Out
D

Pirate Patter

			2 S					
1 C	R	O	W	S	N	E	S	T
U			A					
T			3 B	I	L	G	E	
L		4 B						3 D
2 A	H	O	Y	T	H	E	R	E
S		O						C
S		T		5 P	L	A	N	K
		Y		O				
			4 G	R	U	B		
				T				

Marine Mix-up
1. GAIL 2. BLURP 3. MYRTLE 4. STANLEY

Cave Counting
There are 14 Valley Mermaids

Page 48

Captain Codswallop's Crossword

				1 G												
		2 H	O	O	K											
		A		O							3 B	4 E	A	R	D	
		T		E		5 P			6 L			Y				
				Y		L		7 L	A	N	T	E	R	N		
				G		A			D			P				
8 C	A	P	T	A	I	N	C	O	D	S	W	A	L	L	O	P
				L		K			E			T				
				L					R			C				
9 P	E	G	L	E	G						10 S	H	A	R	K	
				O												
				N												

Page 50

Find The Fishie

Pages 54-55

Pirate Paradise

Pages 56-57

The Duster of Destiny

1.	**A**	6.	**A**
2.	**C**	7.	**B**
3.	**C**	8.	**A**
4.	**B**	9.	**C**
5.	**A**	10.	**B**